# ALL THIS INSIDE...



LB Little Brother BOOKS

Published 2021.
Little Brother Books Ltd, Ground Floor,
23 Southernhay East, Exeter, Devon, EX1 1QL
Printed in Turkey.
books@littlebrotherbooks.co.uk
www.littlebrotherbooks.co.uk


## COUNT IT!

How many flying reptiles can you find on this page?

ANSWER ON PAGE 48

# TOP 10 FACTS

**Find out more about the biggest creatures to ever walk the Earth with these roar-some dinosaur facts.**

1. Dinosaurs ruled the world for nearly 170 million years. **MIND-BLOWING!**

2. The word dinosaur means 'terrible lizard'.

3. Around 800 different dinosaurs have been identified. Scientists still think there are a lot more still to be discovered. **AWESOME!**

4. Although some were ginormous, most dinosaurs were only about the size of a human.

5. The birds that live on Earth today are related to the dinosaurs. **COOL!**

6 Dinosaurs lived on every continent of the world.

NORTH AMERICA
EUROPE
ASIA
AFRICA
SOUTH AMERICA
AUSTRALIA

7 There are dinosaur names beginning with every letter of the alphabet, apart from X.

8 Most dinosaurs were plant-eaters and would rather eat a leaf than each other!

9 All dinosaurs hatched from eggs. Even the ones that grew up to be huge!

10 Nobody knows for sure what colour dinosaurs were, but it's likely they were brown or green to blend in with the trees.

# TRICERATOPS TRAIL

This tired Triceratops needs a nap. Draw a path to lead it home, completing the activities along the way.

Avoid the hungry T-Rex.

2 Count the leaves.
3 Draw some eggs
in the dinosaur nest.
FINISH

# TYRANNOSAURUS

(tye-RAN-oh-sore-us)

**Meet the terrifying T-Rex, the most famous dinosaur of all!**

## Dino fact file

MEANING OF NAME: Tyrant Lizard

SIZE: 12m

HABITAT: Forests and swamps

FOOD: Meat

TIME PERIOD: Cretaceous

## Down in One

Tyrannosaurus had a huge skull and massive jaws, helping this mighty beast swallow small dinosaurs whole. **GULP!**

## Fast Runner

It may have been big but the Tyrannosaurus was speedy for its size. Only the super quick dinos escaped this giant predator.

**FIERCE RATING**

## Tiny Arms

Tyrannosaurus had very small arms compared to the rest of its body. The reason for these titchy limbs has baffled scientists.

My strong, sharp teeth could crunch through bone as easily as you crunch a cookie!

## Did you know?

A T-Rex eyeball was as big as a clenched fist.

# T-REX TRAILS

Which trail leads this hungry dino to his dinner?

a

b

c

ANSWER ON PAGE 48

# PREHISTORIC PUZZLE

There are eight differences between these two dino pictures. Can you be a super spotter and find them all?

Found all 8 changes? Then award yourself the Super Spotter badge!

ANSWERS ON PAGE 48

# DIPLODOCUS

(DIP-low-DOCK-us)

**This huge dino was one of the longest animals to ever roam the Earth.**

## Dino fact file

**MEANING OF NAME:** Double Beam

**SIZE:** 25m

**HABITAT:** Plains

**FOOD:** Leaves

**TIME PERIOD:** Jurassic

## Rumbly Tummy

Hungry Diplodocus ate tough plants that were hard to digest, so they swallowed stones to help break down the leaves inside their stomachs.. **YUCK!**

## Loooooong Neck

Diplodocus had a very long neck, like a giraffe. Some scientists think it wouldn't have been able to hold its small head up high.

**FIERCE RATING**

## Did you know?

**A Diplodocus was as long as two buses.**

# EGG HUNT

Can you help the mummy Diplodocus find 3 more eggs for her nest, hidden somewhere on these pages?

ANSWERS ON PAGE 48

# LET'S EXPLORE

You're off on a dinosaur expedition! Finish the crossword to find out what you need to take with you.

| | | | | | | | | | | | |
|---|---|---|---|---|---|---|---|---|---|---|---|
| | | | | | | | | | | | |
| | i | | o | c | u | l | a | r | s | | |
| | | o | | | | | t | | | | |
| | a | t | | | | | | e | n | | i | l | l |
| | | e | | | | | r | | a | | |
| | | p | | | | | | | m | | |
| | | a | | | | | | | e | | |
| | | d | | | | | | | r | | |
| | | | | | | | | | a | | |

Colour this dinosaur in when you have finished.



ANSWERS ON PAGE 48

DINOSAUR KING
Add fierce colours to this mighty T-Rex. ROAR!
SPOT IT!
Can you find this footprint fossil?

# TRICERATOPS

(tri-SERRA-tops)

**This horned dino knew how to defend itself!**

## Dino fact file

**MEANING OF NAME:** Three-horned face

**SIZE:** 9m

**HABITAT:** Forests

**FOOD:** Plants

**TIME PERIOD:** Cretaceous

### Big and Strong

The chunky Triceratops were as big as an elephant. With their horns and bulky bodies, they looked a bit like rhinos.

### Dino Weapons

Triceratops had three sharp horns. These strong weapons were used for fighting or fending off attackers.

**FIERCE RATING**

## Hard Head

Triceratops had super strong skulls. When they fought each other they would bash their heads together. OUCH!

I had lots of fights with Tyrannosaurus and there are fossils to prove it!

## Did you know?

A Triceratops used its neck frill like a shield.

# SHADOW MATCH

Which of these colourful shadows belongs to the Triceratops?

a

b

c

d

ANSWER ON PAGE 48

# EGG HUNT CHALLENGE

How many of each colour eggs can you spot in this picture? Grab your binoculars and join the hunt!

ANSWERS ON PAGE 48

# PARASAUROLOPHUS

(pa-ra-saw-ROL-off-us)

**This unusual looking dinosaur had a mouth like a duck's beak.**

## Dino fact file

**MEANING OF NAME:** Near Crested Lizard

**SIZE:** 9m

**HABITAT:** Woodlands

**FOOD:** Plants

**TIME PERIOD:** Cretaceous

## Tons of Teeth

Parasaurolophus had hundreds of teeth which they used to grind up plants. Imagine having to clean all of those at bedtime!

## Big Family

Parasaurolophus travelled in large herds. They lived together in woodlands when they weren't on the move.

**FIERCE RATING**

## Boy or Girl?

As well as making a musical sound, the crest on a Parasaurolophus' head helped tell whether the dino was male or female.

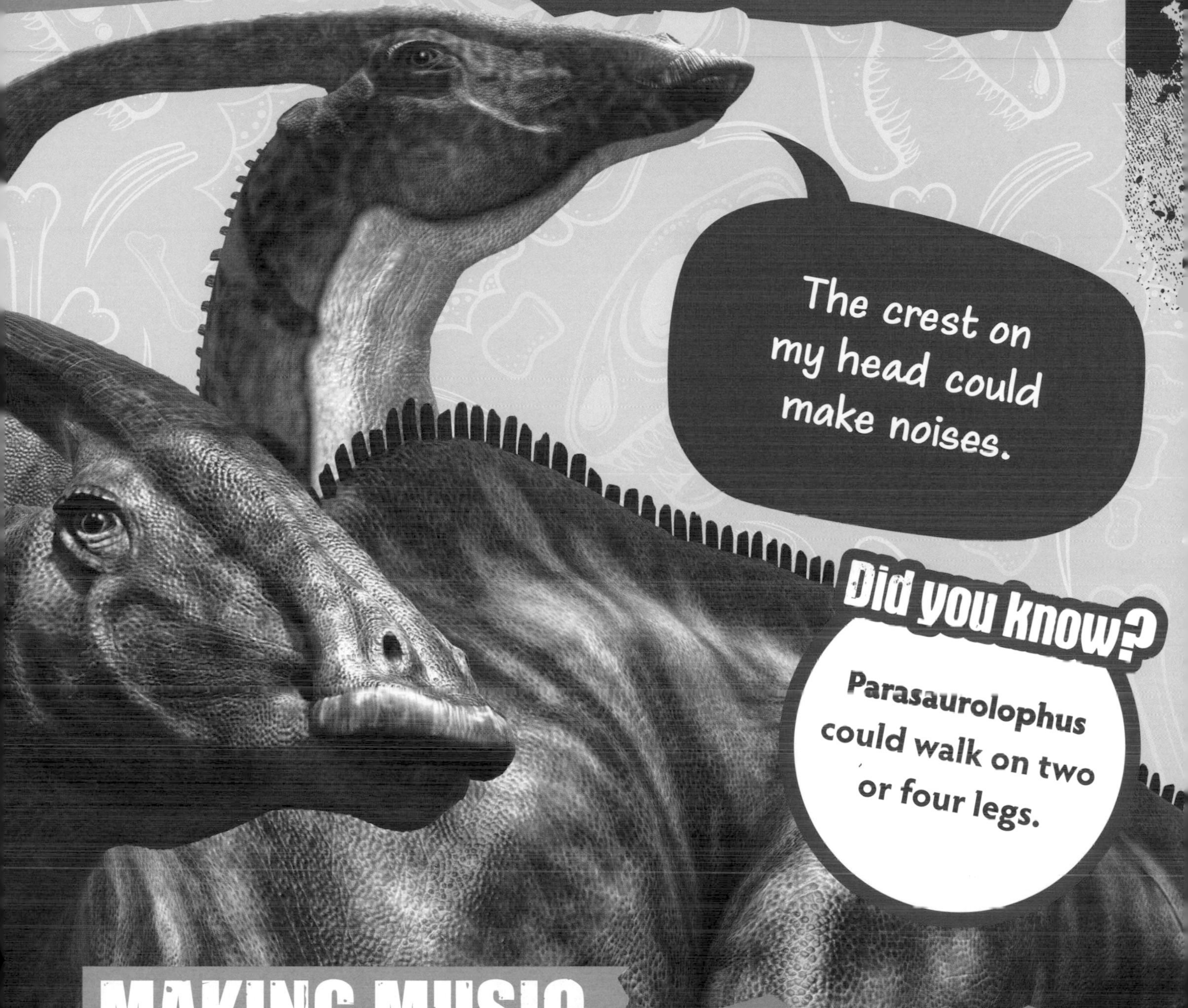

The crest on my head could make noises.

## Did you know?

**Parasaurolophus could walk on two or four legs.**

# MAKING MUSIC

Which instrument did the noise made by a Parasaurolophus crest sound like? Copy the letters into the matching coloured circles to find out.

M T R U P T

ANSWER ON PAGE 48

# DINO DISCOVERY

Imagine you're an explorer and you've just discovered a new dinosaur. Fill in this page all about your exciting find.

## DINOSAUR REPORT

Draw a picture of your dinosaur here.

My dinosaur is called

.....................................osaurus.

Tick where your dinosaur lives

Circle what it likes to eat.

Colour how many cars long your dinosaur is.

Circle the words that best describe your dinosaur.

FIERCE FRIENDLY FAST POWERFUL SCARY

# HELP ME HOME

Can you lead this mummy Oviraptor back to its nest, collecting all the eggs along the way?

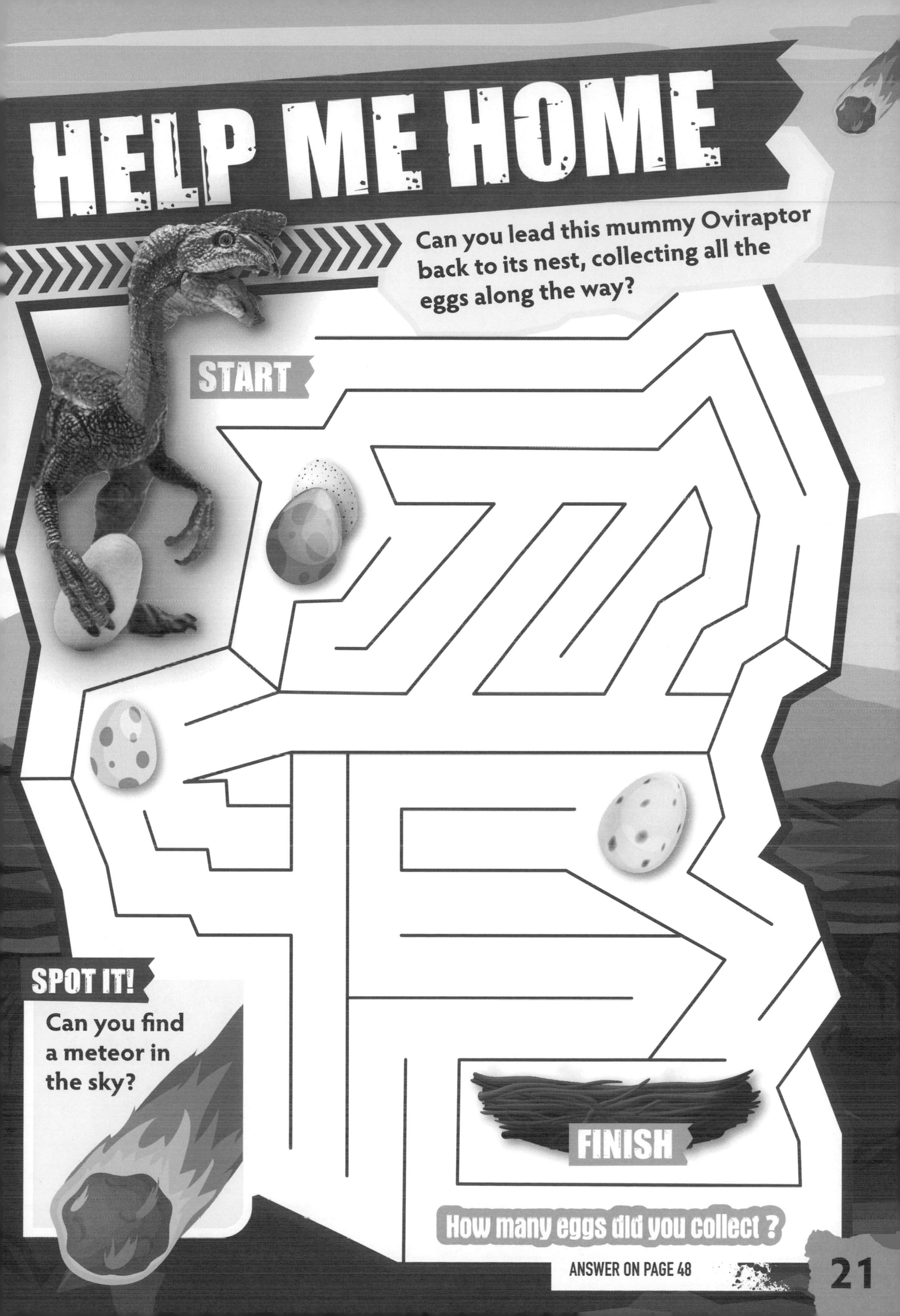


**SPOT IT!**

Can you find a meteor in the sky?

How many eggs did you collect ?

ANSWER ON PAGE 48

# STEGOSAURUS

(STEG-oh-SORE-us)

**A slow-moving, bulky dino with a dangerous tail.**

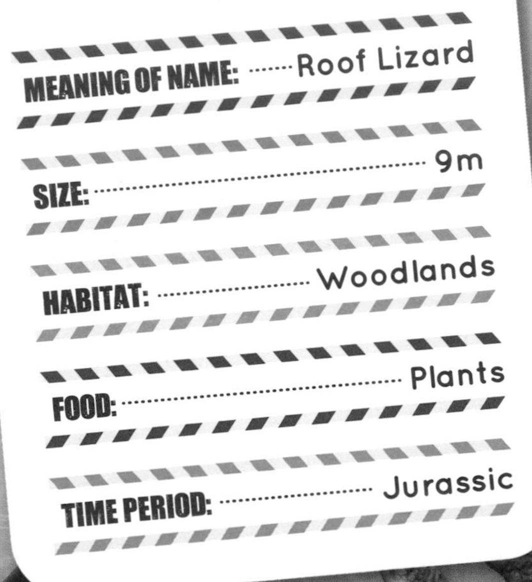

## Dino fact file

MEANING OF NAME: Roof Lizard

SIZE: 9m

HABITAT: Woodlands

FOOD: Plants

TIME PERIOD: Jurassic

### Bony Back Plates

Stegosaurus had two rows of bony plates along its back. Experts think they were just for show, although they may have been used to warn off predators.

### Dumb Dino!

Although the Stegosaurus was the size of an elephant, its brain was no bigger than an apple. It wouldn't have been top of the class at dino school!

FIERCE RATING

## Totally Toothless

Vegetarian Stegosaurus didn't have any teeth. Instead they used their sharp beaks to nibble plants.

My spiked tail was a useful weapon for fending off attackers.

## Did you know?

Stegosaurus' tail spikes could be as long as 1m.

# LEAF COUNT

How many leaves will this starving Stegosaurus munch for lunch?

Answer

ANSWER ON PAGE 48

# MICRORAPTOR

(MIKE-row-rap-tor)

**This tiny bird-like dino was covered in feathers.**

## Dino fact file

MEANING OF NAME: Small thief

SIZE: 40m

HABITAT: Woodlands

FOOD: Small animals

TIME PERIOD: Cretaceous

### Mini Dino

The Microraptor holds the record for smallest dinosaur. It was about the size of a rabbit, but not as cute!

### Dinnertime

Microraptors used their sharp teeth and claws to hunt small animals. Insects, lizards and small mammals were all on their menu.

FIERCE RATING

I couldn't fly but I used feathered arms and legs to glide between trees.

## Useful Tail

The Microraptor had a fan of feathers at the end of its tail. These may have helped the dino keep its balance as it glided through the air.

Lots of **Microraptor** fossils have been found in China.

# TRUE OR FALSE?

The Microraptor could fly.
Circle the right answer.

True

False

ANSWER ON PAGE 48

# DINOSAUR TRAILS

Use a pencil to trace the trails these stomping dinosaurs have left behind.

STOMP!

STOMP!

ZOOM!

ZOOM!

BOOM!

BOOM!

Draw your own trail for the slow-moving Stegosaurus.

ROAR!

ROAR!

THE DINOSAUR KING IS HERE!

FOLLOW THE SPEEDY VELOCIRAPTOR!

IT'S THE GIANT DIPLODOCUS!

FOLLOW THAT SOUND!

# SPINOSAURUS

(SPINE-oh-SORE-us)

**This dragon-like dino was super big.**

## Dino fact file

| | |
|---|---|
| MEANING OF NAME: | Thorn Lizard |
| SIZE: | 16m |
| HABITAT: | Swamps |
| FOOD: | Fish |
| TIME PERIOD: | Cretaceous |

### Super Sail

The Spinosaurus had an eye-catching, bony sail on its back. Scientists think the sail may have helped cool the dinosaur down.

### Duck Feet

Spinosaurus lived in swamplands. It had webbed feet, like a duck, to help it walk through shallow water.

**FIERCE RATING**

## Fishing Time

Hungry Spinosaurus feasted on giant fish. They waded into the water to catch their dinner with their crocodile-like teeth.

I was bigger than the terrifying T-Rex.

## Did you know?

**Spinosaurus was the biggest meat-eating dinosaur.**

# BIG AND SMALL

Can you tick the biggest Spinosaurus and cross out the smallest?

a

b

c

ANSWERS ON PAGE 48

# CREATIVE ZONE

## PAPER PLATE DINO

Step by Step

This paper plate dino is so easy to make and looks totally roar-some!

Adult guidance is needed for this activity

**1** Cut the paper plate in half. Put one half aside to use as the body.

**2** Draw a head and a tail on the other half of the plate and cut them out.

**3** Glue the tail and head to the body. Now your dino is really taking shape.

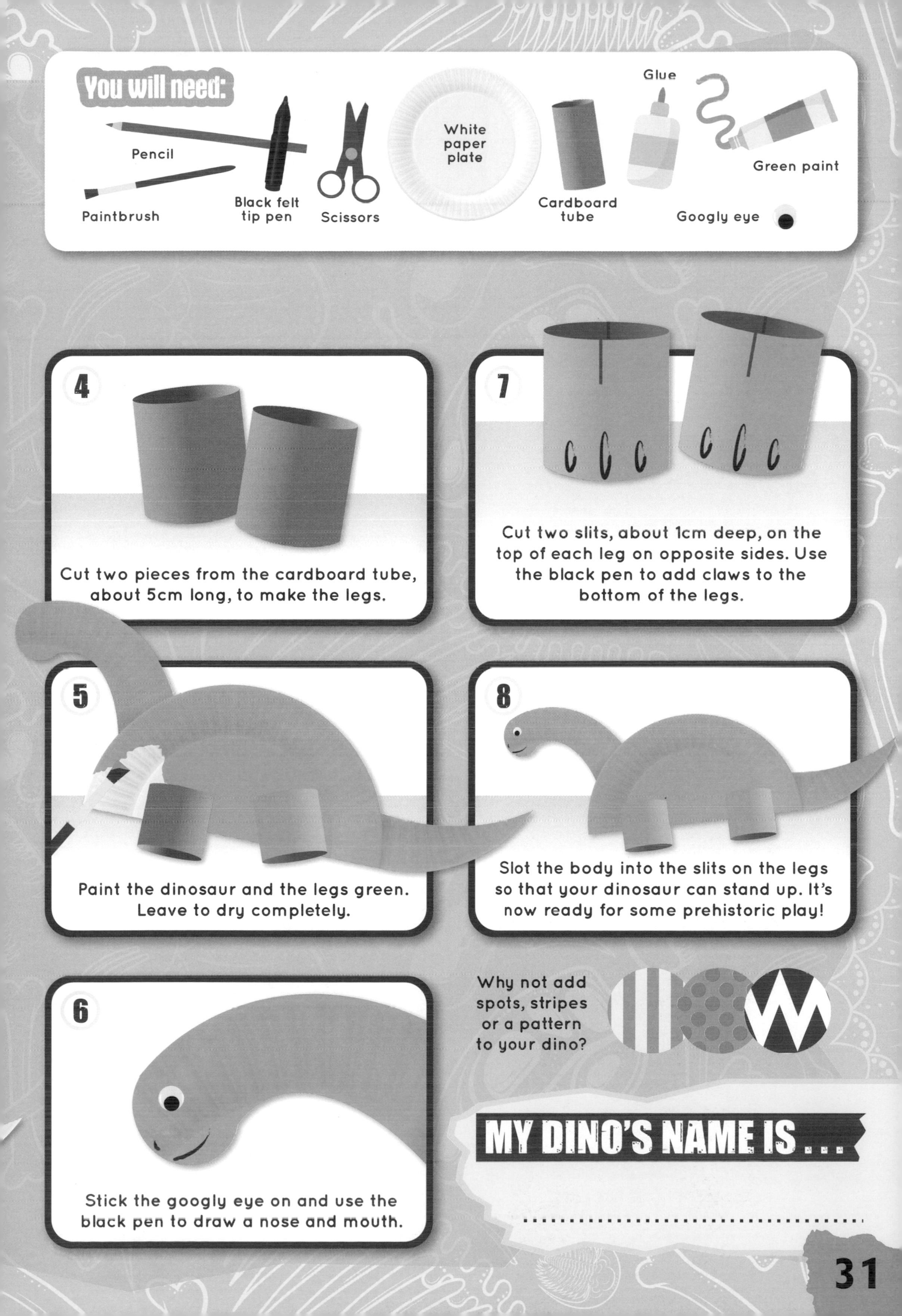

## You will need:

- Pencil
- Paintbrush
- Black felt tip pen
- Scissors
- White paper plate
- Cardboard tube
- Glue
- Green paint
- Googly eye

**4** Cut two pieces from the cardboard tube, about 5cm long, to make the legs.

**5** Paint the dinosaur and the legs green. Leave to dry completely.

**6** Stick the googly eye on and use the black pen to draw a nose and mouth.

**7** Cut two slits, about 1cm deep, on the top of each leg on opposite sides. Use the black pen to add claws to the bottom of the legs.

**8** Slot the body into the slits on the legs so that your dinosaur can stand up. It's now ready for some prehistoric play!

Why not add spots, stripes or a pattern to your dino?

## MY DINO'S NAME IS . . .

..............................................

# ANKYLOSAURUS

(an-KIE-loh-sore-us)

**Meet the tough dino built like a tank.**

## Dino fact file

MEANING OF NAME: Stiff Lizard

SIZE: 10 m

HABITAT: Plains

FOOD: Plants

TIME PERIOD: Cretaceous

### Dangerous Tail

Ankylosaurus had a dangerous built-in weapon – its tail! The end had a bony club so when swung at attackers it would've really hurt. **OW!**

### Body Armour

Ankylosaurus were covered from head to toe in thick plates, spikes and studs. This armour, along with their bulky bodies, made them as tough as tanks.

### FIERCE RATING

## Hungry Dino

Ankylosaurus swallowed its food whole rather than chewing it. It ate plants which were broken down inside its stomach.

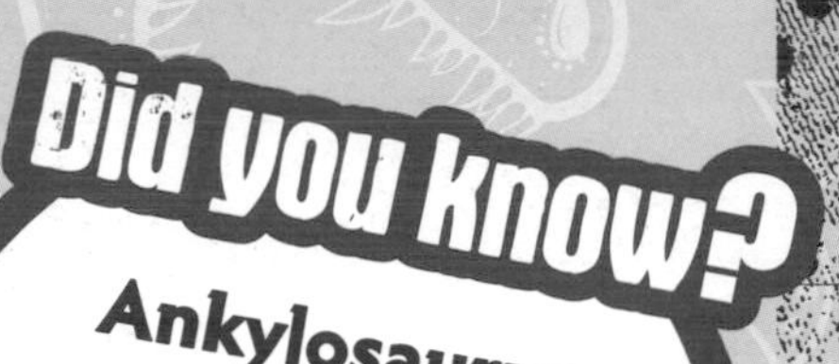


**Ankylosaurus** lived in Canada and the USA 74-67 million years ago.

I was as long as two cars and wider than I was tall.

## LUNCHTIME

Ankylosaurus has snipped some leaves for lunch. How many can you count on these pages?

ANSWER ON PAGE 48

# FOSSIL FUN

Look closely at these fantastic dinosaur fossils. Can you spot the odd one out in each row?

## COUNT IT!

How many dino footprints can you count?

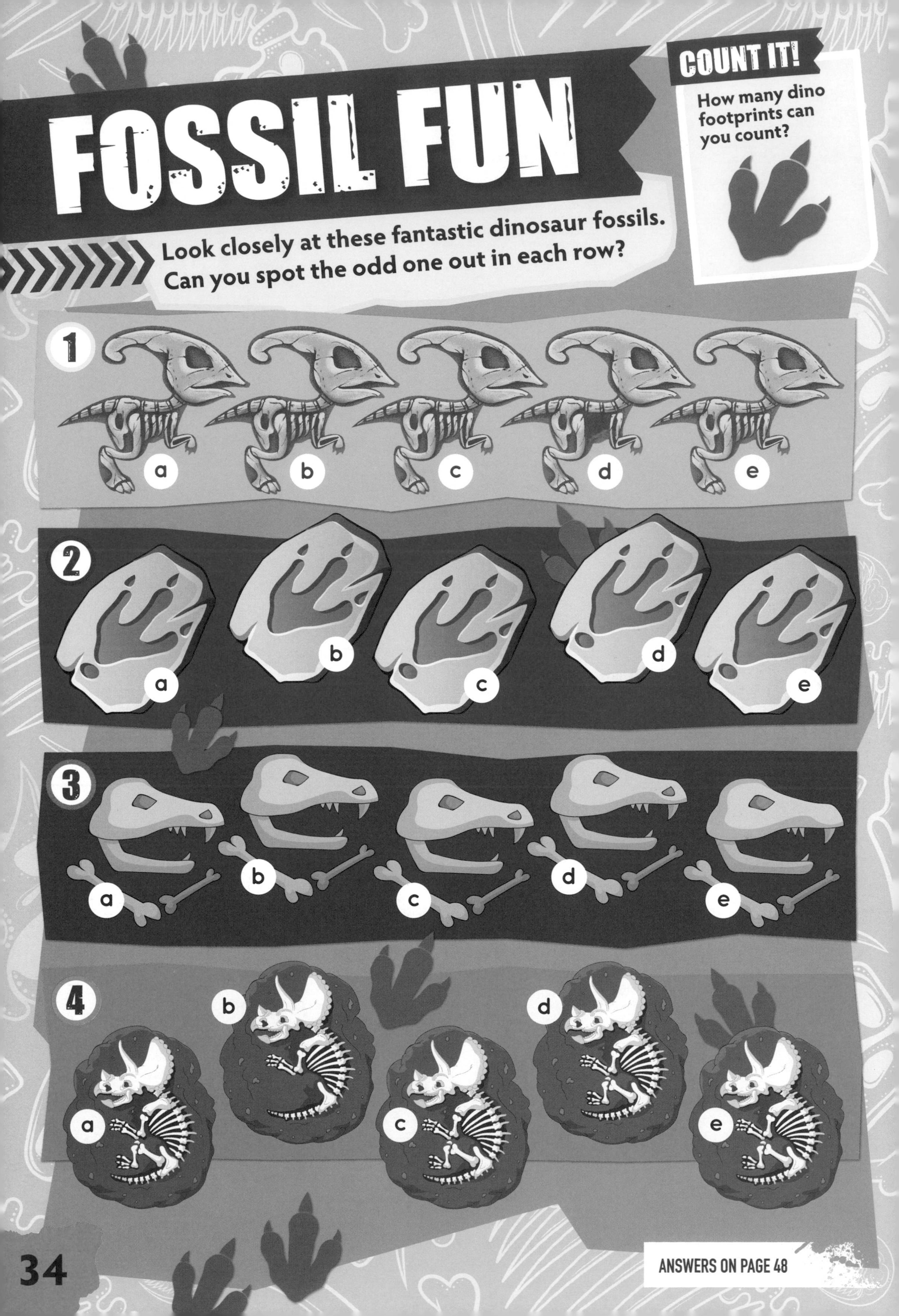




ANSWERS ON PAGE 48

# DOODLE DESIGN

Create your own dinosaur by decorating the dino doodle below. How it looks is completely up to you! **AWESOME!**

# VELOCIRAPTOR

(vel-OSS-ee-rap-tor)

**Introducing Velociraptor, the small but deadly speed thief.**

## Dino fact file

| | |
|---|---|
| MEANING OF NAME: | Speed thief |
| SIZE: | 2m |
| HABITAT: | Deserts |
| FOOD: | Meat |
| TIME PERIOD: | Cretaceous |

### Deadly Claws

Velociraptor's mouth was packed full of razor-sharp teeth. It also had three sharp claws on each hand and foot.

### Fast Runner

Velociraptors were small but they were fast on their feet. Scientists think they may have been able to run as fast as 40 mph – that's as quick as a tiger.

**FIERCE RATING**

## Team Work

Aggressive Velociraptors hunted in packs. Experts think they may have jumped onto the back of their prey and slashed it with their claws. **OUCH!**

I was only the size of a large dog but I was a fierce hunter.

**Velociraptor's long tail helped it keep balance as it ran.**

## ODD ONE OUT

Can you spot the Velociraptor that is different?

a

b

c

ANSWER ON PAGE 48

# JURASSIC JOURNEY

## ACTION BOARD GAME

Race your friends to the volcano in this exciting game of chance.

START 1 2 3 4 5 6 7 8 9 10 11 12 13

Scissors

A counter for each player

A small bag or box

### How to play

1. Carefully cut out the tickets opposite, fold them in half and put them in a bag or box so you can't see what's written on them. Make sure you read page 40 before you cut your tickets out!

2. Take it in turns to pull a ticket out of the bag and follow the instructions.

3. After each turn, fold the ticket up again and put it back in the bag.

4. The first player to reach the volcano wins!

16
17
18
15
19
14
20
22
25
24
23
26
27
28
29
FINISH
Roar like a TYRANNOSAURUS and move forwards 5 spaces.
Stomp like a TRICERATOPS and move back 1 space.
Flap like a MICRORAPTOR and pick another ticket.
Stretch like a DIPLODOCUS and move forward 6 spaces.
Run like a COELOPHYSIS and move to the next red space.
Adult guidance is needed for this activity

# OVIRAPTOR

(OH-vee-RAP-tor)

**Find out more about the bird-like dinosaur that lived in the desert.**

## Dino fact file

MEANING OF NAME: Egg thief

SIZE: 2m

HABITAT: Desert

FOOD: Meat and plants

TIME PERIOD: Cretaceous

### Toothless Dino

Oviraptors didn't have any teeth, which is very unusual for a meat-eating dino. They might have eaten small reptiles and swallowed them whole.

### Wrong Name

Oviraptor got the name 'egg thief' because it was mistakenly thought that it stole eggs from other dinosaurs. A fossil later showed that this wasn't true.

FIERCE RATING

## Safe Home

Fossils have shown that the Oviraptor sat on top of its eggs, like lots of birds do today. It may have had feathered wings to shelter its young.

I couldn't chew but my curved jaw helped me crush hard objects.

The **Oviraptor** laid its eggs in a spiral pattern.

# COLOURFUL EGGS

What colour egg comes next? Colour the white egg the correct colour to finish the sequence.

ANSWER ON PAGE 48

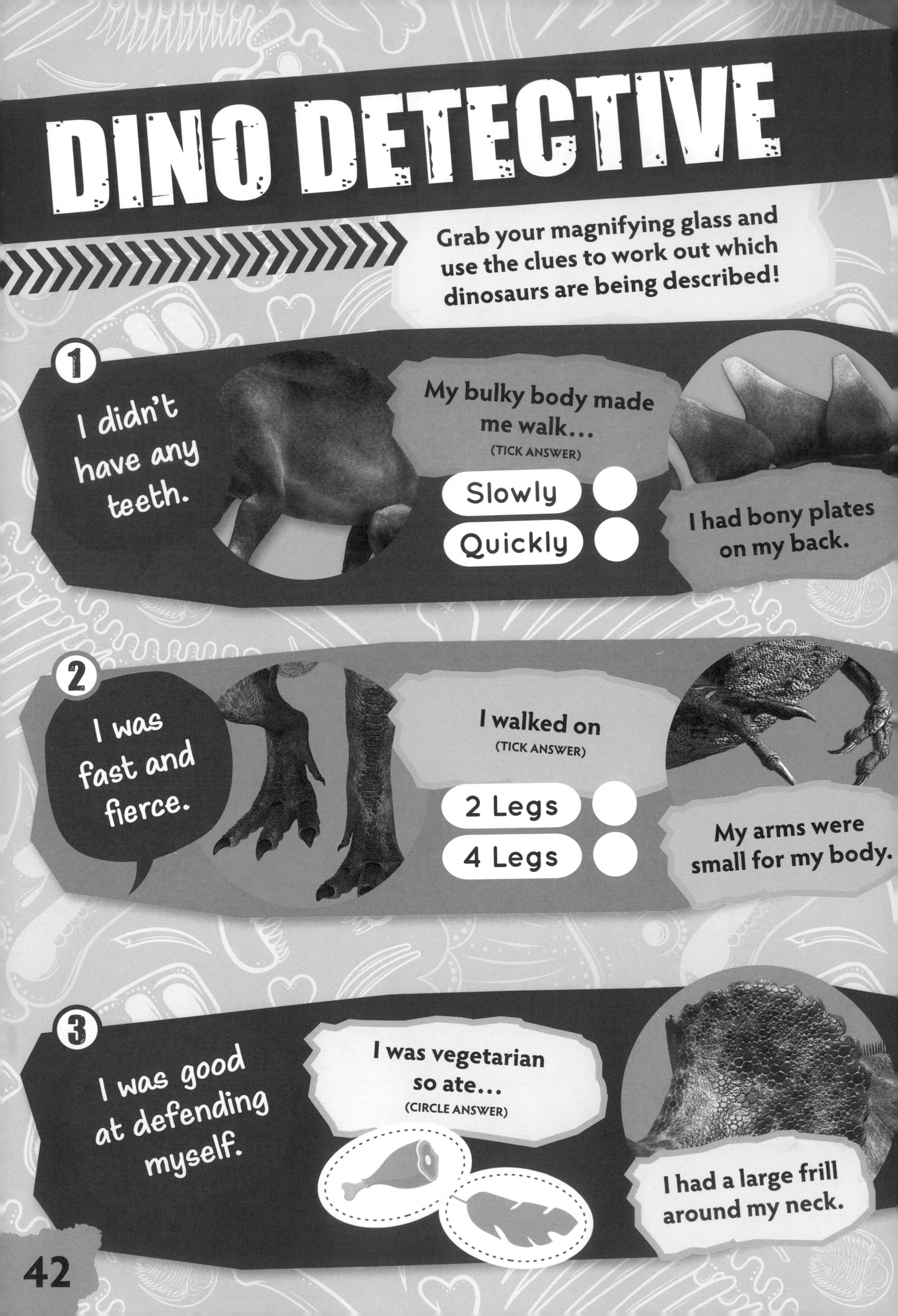

# DINO DETECTIVE

Grab your magnifying glass and use the clues to work out which dinosaurs are being described!

**1**

I didn't have any teeth.

My bulky body made me walk...
(TICK ANSWER)

- Slowly
- Quickly

I had bony plates on my back.

**2**

I was fast and fierce.

I walked on
(TICK ANSWER)

- 2 Legs
- 4 Legs

My arms were small for my body.

**3**

I was good at defending myself.

I was vegetarian so ate...
(CIRCLE ANSWER)

I had a large frill around my neck.

ANSWERS ON PAGE 48

# COELOPHYSIS

(seel-OH--fie-sis)

**Meet one of the Earth's first dinosaurs.**

## Dino fact file

**MEANING OF NAME:** Hollow form

**SIZE:** 3m

**HABITAT:** Desert plains

**FOOD:** Meat

**TIME PERIOD:** Triassic

## Dino Menu

Coelophysis had long, narrow jaws and very sharp teeth. It feasted on insects and small reptiles, such as lizards.

## Long Legs

With its long legs and light body, Coelophysis would have been a fast runner. Imagine having one of those chasing you!

## FIERCE RATING

My speed and fierceness made me an impressive hunter.

## Lots to Learn

These speedy dinos lived and hunted in packs. Scientists think that young Coelophysis may have learnt how to hunt from the adults in their group.

## Did you know?

**Coelophysis had excellent eyesight.**

# UP CLOSE

Which one of these body parts belongs to the Coelophysis?

a

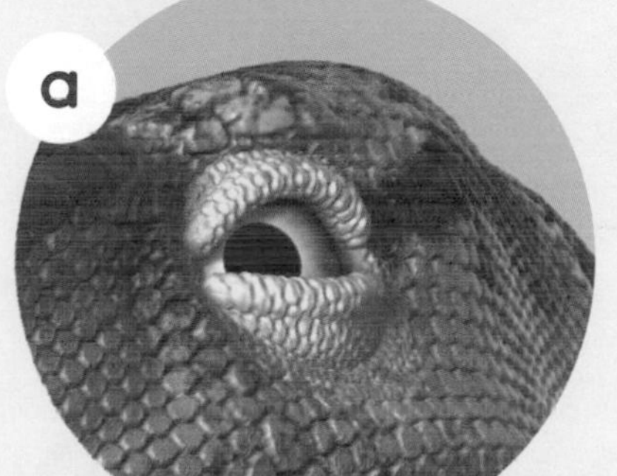

b

c

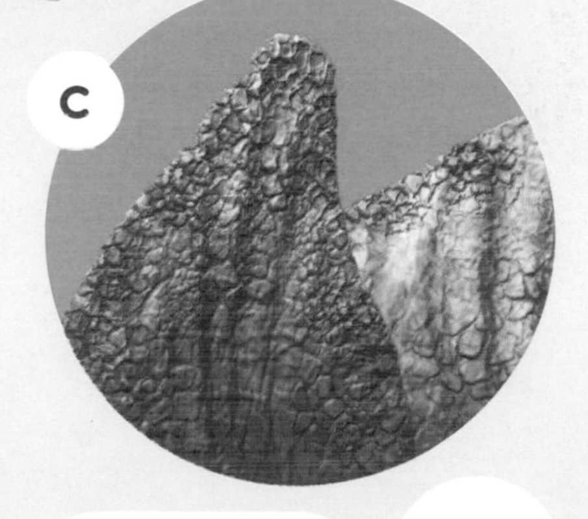

Answer

ANSWER ON PAGE 48

(Al-oh-saw-russ)

**This gigantic predator was a dino to be feared.**

## Dino fact file

**MEANING OF NAME:** Other Lizard

**SIZE:** 12m

**HABITAT:** Woodlands

**FOOD:** Meat

**TIME PERIOD:** Jurassic

### Big Mouth

Allosaurus had a huge mouth to match its massive body. It could open its jaws really wide – handy for taking big bites!

Allosaurus liked to hunt alone. Fossils have shown that those hunting in packs often attacked each other!

## Deadly Predator

The huge Allosaurus was built for hunting It had razor sharp claws, deadly teeth and super speed.

I was a meat-eater and ate anything I could catch!

Allosaurus may have hidden in the bushes and jumped out on its prey.

## FUN FACT

Trace over the word to discover what Allosaurus used to help it balance as it ran.

tail

# ANSWERS

**PAGE 1 - COUNT IT!** There are 4 flying reptiles.

**PAGES 4-5 - TRICERATOPS TRAIL** There are 5 leaves.

**PAGES 6-7 - T-REX TRAILS** b.

**PAGES 8-9 - PREHISTORIC PUZZLE**

**PAGES 10-11 - DIPLODOCUS**

**PAGE 12 - LET'S EXPLORE**

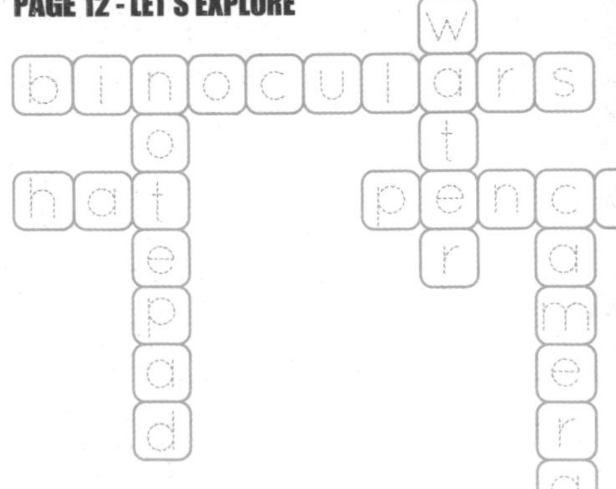


**PAGES 14-15 - SHADOW MATCH** a.

**PAGES 16-17 - EGG HUNT**
Grey - 4, Blue - 3, yellow - 1, Green - 3, Orange - 5.

**PAGES 18-19 - MAKING MUSIC** Trumpet.

**PAGE 21 - HELP ME HOME** 4 eggs to collect on the way.

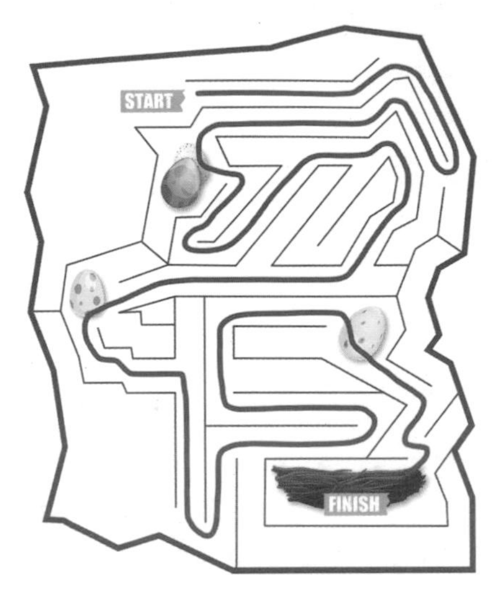


**PAGES 22-23 - LEAF COUNT**
There are 17 leaves.

**PAGES 24-25 - TRUE OR FALSE?** False.

**PAGE 29 - BIG AND SMALL**
biggest – c, smallest – b.

**PAGES 32-33 - LUNCHTIME**
There are 5 leaves.

**PAGE 34 - FOSSIL FUN**
1 - d, 2 - b, 3 - e, 4 - b.
There are 7 dino footprints.

**PAGES 36-37 - ODD ONE OUT** a.

**PAGES 40-41 - COLOURFUL EGGS** Yellow.

**PAGES 42-43 - DINO DETECTIVE**
1 - Stegosaurus, 2 - T-Rex, 3 - Triceratops.

**PAGES 44-45 - UP CLOSE** a.